minions™

Seek and Find

centum

For your googles only!
Check out these other titles:

Minions Sticker book
Minions Long Live King Bob
Minions Fun Book
Minions The Junior Novel
Minions Activity Book

MINIONS: SEEK AND FIND
A CENTUM BOOK 9781910114223

Written by Trey King
Art by Fractured Pixels
Based on the Motion Picture Screenplay by Brian Lynch
Published in Great Britain by Centum Books Ltd

This edition published 2015
2015 © Universal Studios Licensing, LLC.

1 3 5 7 9 10 8 6 4 2

Centum Books Ltd, Unit 1, Upside Station Building, Solsbro Road, Torquay, Devon, UK, TQ2 6FD

books@centumbooksltd.co.uk

CENTUM BOOKS Limited Reg. No. 07641486

A CIP catalogue record for this book is available from the British Library

Printed in Italy

The story of the Minions began at the dawn of time. They started as tiny single-celled organisms but evolved through the ages, getting bigger and yellower.

Minions have always looked to serve the most despicable master. But more often than not, they accidentally killed their masters, so their search is ongoing.

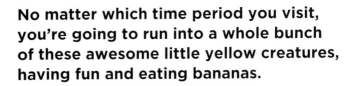

No matter which time period you visit, you're going to run into a whole bunch of these awesome little yellow creatures, having fun and eating bananas.

On the following pages, it'll be up to you to seek and find Minions, weird animals, objects, and more – good luck!

Prehistoric Beach Party!

MINION BEACH

Minions were some of the first creatures to walk the Earth – which means they invented barbecues and pool parties! Check out these crafty and despicable Minion ancestors as they show the world how to have a good time.

CAN YOU SPOT:

- 1 seahorse with a stripe
- 1 yellow fish
- 12 starfish
- 1 Minion with orange goggles
- 29 one-eyed Minions
- 1 jellyfish with six legs
- 1 yellow jellyfish
- 1 coconut

DINOSAUR DINNERTIME!

Dinosaurs are massive creatures that roamed the Earth millions of years ago. The only things bigger than their bodies were their appetites! It's time to eat, so the Minions are making a feast. Care to join them?

CAN YOU SPOT:

- 1 Minion wearing spots
- 3 green bananas
- 1 dino gold tooth
- 1 Minion tower
- 11 pterodactyls (flying winged dinosaurs)
- 1 Minion filing nails
- 1 Minion wearing a hair bow

6

CAVEMAN HANGOUT!

Woolly mammoths, saber-toothed tigers, cavemen – Minions seem to know all the cool (prehistoric) people! Everyone is hanging out and having a good time.

CAN YOU SPOT:

- 1 Minion roasting a marshmallow
- 1 mouse toy
- 1 stuck Minion
- 1 Minion eating popcorn
- 1 Minion sliding
- 6 Minions in spotted clothes
- 1 prehistoric turtle

9

TIME FOR WORK!

Building the pyramids was no easy task – good job that the Minions were around to help out. With all these yellow helpers, the job should be done in no time . . . unless someone makes a mess of things!

CAN YOU SPOT:

- 1 Minion hiding
- 1 Minion reading a book
- 1 Minion dentist
- 1 group of Minions playing limbo
- 2 Minions eating sandwiches
- 1 Minion walking like an Egyptian
- 1 yellow flower
- 6 Minions with hammers

Oh, no, those pirates are taking stuff – what a bunch of bullies! Pirates are well-known for stealing all sorts of things, like gold, precious gems, treasure, princesses and . . . bananas?!

CAN YOU SPOT:
- 7 Minion pirate flags
- 1 message in a bottle
- 5 shark fins
- 1 Minion in scuba gear
- 1 pirate eyeglass
- 5 mice
- 1 Minion with a peg leg
- 1 eyepatch Minion
- 1 Minion with a moustache
- 12 Minions with swords

13

MARCH OF THE MINION ARMY!

At one point, Minions worked under the famous French military leader, Napoleon. Sure, the Minions could have been fighting a battle, but instead, they chose to do things their own way.

CAN YOU SPOT:

- 1 deck of playing cards
- 3 Minions making snow angels
- 1 rolling wheel of cheese
- 1 Minion using a paddle-bat to fight
- 1 Minion ready to be shot out of a cannon
- 5 Minions hiding in the snow
- 1 red star
- 1 blue hat feather

Snow Day!

After so much hard work, Minions deserve a day off. What better way to spend it than building snowmen, snow-women, and snow-Minions!

CAN YOU SPOT:
- 1 harmonica player
- 1 juggling seal
- 2 games of noughts and crosses
- laundry hanging out to dry
- 1 sleepy Minion
- 1 yeti wearing a Santa hat
- blue ice cream
- 1 barefoot Minion

New York City Takeover!

This city is used to tourists from all over the world, but all these tourists look the same! Minions have taken over the 'City That Never Sleeps'. I wonder what they're going to do first . . .

CAN YOU SPOT:

- 1 Minion eating 11 hot dogs
- 2 (normal) dogs
- 1 Minion directing traffic
- Minions playing marbles
- 1 Minion with grandma hair
- 1 Minion with a moustache
- 1 Minion dressed as a hippie
- 3 Minions with bananas
- 1 pair of brown overalls

VILLAIN-CON!

If you're looking for a despicable new master (or just an evil friend to rob banks and toy stores with), then Villain-Con is the place to be. Just watch your wallet closely – in this crowd, it's likely to get stolen!

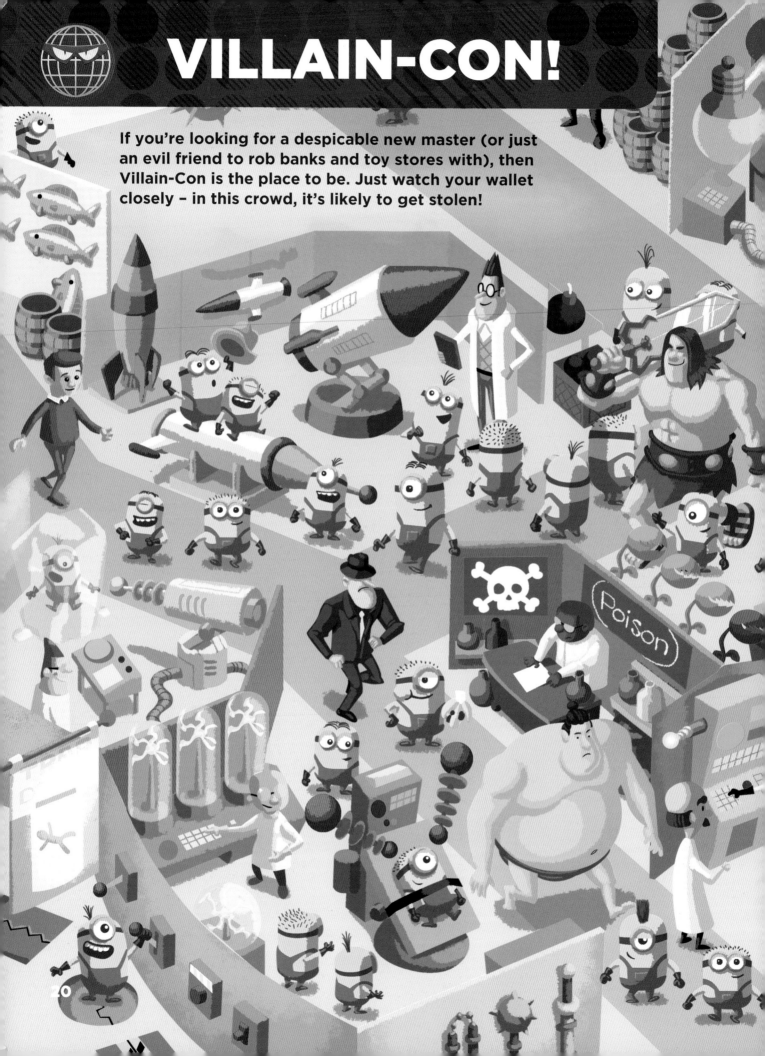

Poison

CAN YOU SPOT:

- 1 skull and crossbones
- 2 Minions eating bananas
- 1 Freeze-ray Gun
- 1 jet pack
- Bob handing out his business card
- 1 pair of green overalls
- 1 red plant
- 1 Minion with a mohawk
- 1 cowboy hat

British Invasion!

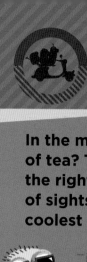

In the mood for fish 'n' chips and a spot of tea? Then the Minions have come to the right place. In London, there's lots of sightseeing to do, but right now, the coolest things to see are Minions!

CAN YOU SPOT:

- Kevin and Stuart riding a moped
- 1 polo-playing Minion riding a dog
- 1 Minion using the phone
- 1 Minion in a bowler hat
- 1 Minion in a bin
- 1 Minion wth blue gloves
- 23 one-eyed Minions
- 8 birds

The End? Nope!

We have a few more things hidden for you. Go back for another look and see if you can spot these extra-fun Minions and others things.

CAN YOU SPOT: 1 Minion wearing starfish

CAN YOU SPOT: 1 Minion in a barrel

CAN YOU SPOT: 1 Minion with a parachute

CAN YOU SPOT: 1 Minion with bunny ears

CAN YOU SPOT: 1 Minion cave painting

CAN YOU SPOT: 1 Minion driving a car

CAN YOU SPOT: 1 Minion with a croc-hunter hat

CAN YOU SPOT: 1 rocket ship ride

CAN YOU SPOT: 1 Minion with a sword in his mouth

CAN YOU SPOT: King Bob!